WeightWatchers®

Mix it
Match it

1000+
Breakfast, Lunch, and Dinner Combinations

About Weight Watchers

Weight Watchers International, Inc. is the world's leading provider of weight management services, operating globally through a network of Company-owned and franchise operations. Weight Watchers holds over 48,000 weekly meetings, where members receive group support and education about healthful eating patterns, behavior modification, and physical activity. Weight-loss and weight-management results vary by individual. We recommend that you attend Weight Watchers meetings to benefit from the supportive environment you'll find there and follow the comprehensive Weight Watchers program, which includes food plans, an activity plan, and a thinking-skills plan. In addition, Weight Watchers offers a wide range of products, publications and programs for those interested in weight loss and weight control. For the Weight Watchers meeting nearest you, call **800-651-6000.** For information on bringing Weight Watchers to your workplace, call **800-8AT-WORK.** Also, visit us at our Web site, **WeightWatchers.com,** or look for *Weight Watchers Magazine* at your newsstand or in your meeting room.

WEIGHT WATCHERS PUBLISHING GROUP

EDITORIAL DIRECTOR	**NANCY GAGLIARDI**
CREATIVE DIRECTOR	**ED MELNITSKY**
PRODUCTION MANAGER	**ALAN BIEDERMAN**
OFFICE MANAGER AND PUBLISHING ASSISTANT	**JENNY LABOY-BRACE**
FOOD EDITOR	**EILEEN RUNYAN**
EDITOR	**ALICE THOMPSON**
NUTRITION CONSULTANT	**PATRICIA SANTELLI**
PHOTOGRAPHER	**ALAN RICHARDSON**
FOOD STYLIST	**MICHAEL PEDERSON**
PROP STYLIST	**DEBRAH E. DONAHUE**
BOOK & COVER DESIGN	**DANIELA HRITCU**

TEX-MEX SHRIMP STEW
(DINNER, *4 POINTS* value)

About Our Recipes

We make every effort to ensure that you will have success with our recipes. For best results and for nutritional accuracy, please keep the following guidelines in mind:

▨ Recipes in this book have been developed for Weight Watchers members who are following either the **Flex Plan** or the **Core Plan**® on **TurnAround.**® All **Core Plan** recipes are marked with our **Core Plan** recipe icon ☑ . We include *POINTS*® values so you can use any of the recipes if you are following the **Flex Plan** on the program. *POINTS* values are assigned based on calories, fat (grams), and fiber (grams) provided for a serving size of a recipe.

▨ All recipes feature approximate nutritional information; our recipes are analyzed for Calories (Cal), Total Fat (Fat), Saturated Fat (Sat Fat), Trans Fat (Trans Fat), Cholesterol (Chol), Sodium (Sod), Carbohydrates (Carb), Dietary Fiber (Fib), Protein (Prot), and Calcium (Calc).

▨ Nutritional information for recipes that include meat, poultry, and fish are based on cooked skinless boneless portions (unless otherwise stated), with the fat trimmed.

▨ We recommend that you buy lean meat and poultry, then trim it of all visible fat before cooking. When poultry is cooked with the skin on, we suggest removing the skin before eating.

▨ We follow the USDA guidelines for cooking meats and poultry to safe temperatures to prevent foodborne illness, but for beef and lamb (steaks, roasts, and chops) be aware that cooking them to the recommended minimum of 145°F will give you a medium-cooked steak, roast, or chop.

▨ Before serving, divide foods—including vegetables, sauce, or accompaniments—into portions of equal size according to the designated number of servings per recipe.

▨ Any substitutions made to the ingredients will alter the "Per serving" nutritional information and may affect the **Core Plan** recipe status or the *POINTS* value.

▨ All fresh fruits, vegetables, and greens in recipes should be rinsed before using.

Introduction

Welcome to the new, improved Weight Watchers **TurnAround**® program and our easy-to-use **Mix It, Match It** cookbook. We've developed it to help you plan delicious healthful meals—at a glance.

Simply flip through the pages to find a combination of meals that appeals to you and fits your daily ***POINTS***® target. Whether you follow the **Flex Plan** or the **Core Plan**®, you'll find recipes to help you manage your weight and stay motivated.

As you mix and match our breakfasts, lunches, dinners, and snacks each day, be aware that though most of the combinations meet the Weight Watchers Good Health Guidelines, it's still a good idea to use your paper Quik Trak™ System or eTools Plan Manager to keep track of your ***POINTS***® values.

Enjoy every delicious recipe!

CONTENTS

BARBECUED DRUMSTICKS
(DINNER, *4 POINTS* value)

breakfast

lunch

dinner

New York–Style Eggs and Lox

PREP 5 MINUTES   COOK 10 MINUTES   SERVES 4

1 Heat the oil in a large nonstick skillet over medium heat. Add the onion and cook, stirring frequently, until golden, about 7 minutes. Meanwhile, whisk the eggs, egg whites, milk, salt, and pepper in a small bowl until frothy.

2 Raise the heat to medium-high. Pour the egg mixture over the onion; cook undisturbed about 15 seconds. Add the lox and cook, stirring frequently, until the eggs are set, about 30 seconds. Divide evenly among 4 plates. Top each serving with 1 tablespoon sour cream and sprinkle with the scallions.

PER SERVING (about $2/3$ cup scrambled-egg mixture and 1 tablespoon sour cream): 115 Cal, 4 g Fat, 1 g Sat Fat, 0 g Trans Fat, 113 mg Chol, 767 mg Sod, 5 g Carb, 1 g Fib, 14 g Prot, 61 mg Calc. **POINTS** value: **2.**

Turkey, Orange, and Fennel Salad

PREP 15 MINUTES   COOK NONE   SERVES 4

1 Whisk together the oil, vinegar, orange zest, mustard, and salt in a small bowl. Set aside.

2 Toss together the lettuce and fennel in a salad bowl. Top with the turkey, tomato, and onion. Arrange the orange slices around the edge of the bowl. Drizzle with the dressing. Toss just before serving.

PER SERVING (about 3 cups): 184 Cal, 6 g Fat, 1 g Sat Fat, 0 g Trans Fat, 47 mg Chol, 343 mg Sod, 15 g Carb, 5 g Fib, 20 g Prot, 83 mg Calc. **POINTS** value: **3.**

Pomegranate-Glazed Shish Kebabs

PREP 10 MINUTES   COOK 10 MINUTES   SERVES 4

1 Spray the broiler rack with nonstick spray; preheat the broiler.

2 Combine the broth, pomegranate molasses, and salt in a small bowl.

3 Thread the beef and vegetables on 4 (12-inch) metal skewers, alternating the beef and the vegetables. Brush with half the broth mixture. Place the skewers on the broiler rack and broil 5 inches from the heat for 4 minutes. Turn and brush with the remaining broth mixture. Broil until the meat and vegetables are browned and cooked though, 5–6 minutes. Garnish with pomegranate seeds if using.

PER SERVING (1 skewer): 189 Cal, 6 g Fat, 2 g Sat Fat, 1 g Trans Fat, 63 mg Chol, 671 mg Sod, 10 g Carb, 2 g Fib, 24 g Prot, 26 mg Calc. **POINTS** value: **4.**

2   cups fresh or thawed frozen unsweetened
     blueberries
¼   cup confectioners' sugar
2   tablespoons water
⅛   teaspoon cinnamon
2   cups old-fashioned rolled oats
2   tablespoons packed brown sugar
1½   teaspoons baking powder
½   teaspoon baking soda
¼   teaspoon salt
1   cup plain low-fat yogurt
⅔   cup unsweetened apple juice
2   large eggs, lightly beaten
½   teaspoon vanilla extract

¼   cup finely chopped red onion
4   small black olives, pitted and chopped
1   tablespoon chopped fresh basil
2   teaspoons red-wine vinegar
2   teaspoons olive oil
1   (7-inch) crusty hero roll, split
2   ounces thinly sliced deli chicken or turkey
1   ounce (2 slices) thinly sliced prosciutto
1   bottled roasted red bell pepper, cut into
     fourths

2   teaspoons Asian (dark) sesame oil
2   garlic cloves, minced
1   tablespoon minced peeled fresh ginger
5   cups low-sodium vegetable broth or
     fish stock
2   tablespoons light miso paste
Pinch cayenne
6   ounces soba noodles or thin spaghetti
1   pound sea scallops
1   (6-ounce) bag baby spinach leaves
3   scallions, sliced

snacks

Salmon Dip with Cucumbers

PREP 10 MINUTES   COOK NONE   SERVES 6

¼ pound smoked salmon, chopped
1 (8-ounce) container fat-free sour cream
1 tablespoon chopped fresh dill
1½ teaspoons prepared horseradish
1 teaspoon lemon juice
⅛ teaspoon black pepper
2 cucumbers, cut into rounds

Put half the salmon, the sour cream, dill, horseradish, lemon juice, and pepper in a food processor or blender; pulse just to combine. Transfer to a small bowl, stir in the remaining salmon, and serve with the cucumber rounds.

PER SERVING (¼ cup dip and ½ cup cucumber rounds): 56 Cal, 1 g Fat, 0 g Sat Fat, 0 g Trans Fat, 4 mg Chol, 434 mg Sod, 6 g Carb, 1 g Fib, 5 g Prot, 63 mg Calc. *POINTS* value: *1.*

Stuffed Plum Tomatoes

PREP 15 MINUTES   COOK NONE   SERVES 6

6 small plum tomatoes
1 cup fat-free cottage cheese
1 tablespoon minced scallion
1 tablespoon chopped fresh basil
2 teaspoons grated lemon zest
¼ teaspoon salt
⅛ teaspoon black pepper

1 Halve the tomatoes lengthwise. Using your fingers, pull out and discard the seeds; scoop out the flesh with a spoon or a melon baller and place it in a medium bowl.

2 Add the remaining ingredients to the bowl and stir until well blended. Spoon the mixture into the tomato halves, mounding to fill. Serve at once or cover with plastic wrap and refrigerate up to 4 hours.

PER SERVING (2 stuffed tomato halves): 37 Cal, 0 g Fat, 0 g Sat Fat, 0 g Trans Fat, 2 mg Chol, 248 mg Sod, 4 g Carb, 1 g Fib, 5 g Prot, 31 mg Calc. *POINTS* value: *1.*

SALMON DIP
WITH CUCUMBERS,

STUFFED
PLUM TOMATOES,

CITRUS-SNAPPER
SEVICHE, PAGE 63

Quick Avocado Salsa

1   medium ripe avocado, halved, pitted, peeled, and diced
¼   seedless cucumber, diced
⅓   cup fat-free salsa
1   tablespoon chopped fresh cilantro
¼   teaspoon salt

Put the avocado, cucumber, salsa, cilantro, and salt in a medium bowl and toss to combine. Serve at once or cover and refrigerate up to 8 hours.

PER SERVING (⅓ cup): 54 Cal, 4 g Fat, 1 g Sat Fat, 0 g Trans Fat, 0 mg Chol, 162 mg Sod, 4 g Carb, 2 g Fib, 1 g Prot, 11 mg Calc. **POINTS** value: **1.**

Spiced Edamame

1   teaspoon canola oil
1   garlic clove
1   teaspoon grated peeled fresh ginger
⅛   teaspoon crushed red pepper
1   (10-ounce) package frozen shelled edamame (green soybeans), thawed
⅛   teaspoon salt

Heat the oil in a nonstick skillet over medium-high heat. Add the garlic, ginger, and crushed red pepper; cook, stirring, until fragrant, about 30 seconds. Add the edamame and salt; cook, stirring frequently, until heated through, about 4 minutes.

PER SERVING (about ½ cup): 76 Cal, 4 g Fat, 0 g Sat Fat, 0 g Trans Fat, 0 mg Chol, 54 mg Sod, 6 g Carb, 2 g Fib, 6 g Prot, 70 mg Calc. **POINTS** value: **1.**

Stuffed Portobello Mushroom Caps

PREP 8 MINUTES   COOK 30 MINUTES   SERVES 4

1½ teaspoons olive oil
2 garlic cloves, minced
1 (5-ounce) bag baby spinach
6 tablespoons water
¼ cup plain dried bread crumbs
2 ounces lean cooked ham, finely diced
1½ tablespoons pine nuts
4 Portobello mushrooms, stems discarded and caps wiped clean

1 Preheat the oven to 425°F. Spray a large baking dish with nonstick spray.

2 Heat the oil in a large nonstick skillet over medium heat. Add the garlic and cook, stirring constantly, until fragrant, about 1 minute. Add the spinach and 3 tablespoons of the water. Cook, stirring occasionally, until the spinach wilts, about 4 minutes. Remove from the heat. Stir in the bread crumbs, ham, and pine nuts.

3 Place the mushroom caps in the baking dish, gill sides up. Fill the caps with the spinach mixture, mounding it slightly. Add the remaining 3 tablespoons water to the baking dish. Bake until the mushrooms are tender and the filling is hot, about 25 minutes.

PER SERVING (1 mushroom): 115 Cal, 4 g Fat, 1 g Sat Fat, 0 g Trans Fat, 7 mg Chol, 315 mg Sod, 12 g Carb, 3 g Fib, 6 g Prot, 40 mg Calc. **POINTS** value: **2.**

Citrus-Snapper Seviche (pictured)

PREP 15 MINUTES   COOK NONE   SERVES 4

¾ pound very fresh skinless red snapper, tilapia, or flounder fillets, cut into ¼-inch dice
¼ cup lime juice
12 grape tomatoes, chopped
1 orange, peeled and diced
¼ cup diced red onion
½ teaspoon salt
⅛ teaspoon cayenne
2 tablespoons chopped fresh cilantro
12 Belgian endive leaves

1 Combine the snapper and lime juice in a medium bowl; toss to coat and set aside while preparing the other ingredients. Add the tomatoes, orange, onion, salt, and cayenne. Refrigerate, covered, about 10 minutes.

2 Toss with the cilantro. Spoon the seviche evenly into the endive leaves and serve at once.

PER SERVING (3 filled endive leaves): 116 Cal, 1 g Fat, 0 g Sat Fat, 0 g Trans Fat, 45 mg Chol, 380 mg Sod, 9 g Carb, 3 g Fib, 17 g Prot, 48 mg Calc. **POINTS** value: **2.**

Shrimp and Jicama Cocktail Kebabs

PREP 12 MINUTES   COOK 15 MINUTES   SERVES 4

16 large shrimp, peeled and deveined
2 tablespoons lime juice
4 teaspoons honey
2 teaspoons olive oil
2 teaspoons apple-cider vinegar
2 teaspoons Dijon mustard
1 tablespoon chopped fresh cilantro
¼ teaspoon salt
1 small jicama, peeled and cut into 16 chunks
8 cherry tomatoes, halved
2 cups mixed baby salad greens

1 Bring a medium saucepan of water to a boil; add the shrimp. Reduce the heat and simmer just until the shrimp are opaque in the center, 3–4 minutes. Drain and rinse under cold running water to stop the cooking. Pat dry with paper towels.

2 Combine the lime juice, honey, oil, vinegar, mustard, cilantro, and salt in a bowl and whisk until blended. Add the shrimp, jicama, and tomatoes and toss to coat.

3 Thread 2 shrimp, 2 pieces of jicama, and 2 tomato halves on each of 8 (6-inch) wooden skewers; reserve any vinaigrette remaining in the bowl. Divide the greens among 4 goblets; place 2 kebabs in each goblet and drizzle with the reserved vinaigrette.

PER SERVING (2 kebabs, 2 tablespoons vinaigrette, and ½ cup greens): 114 Cal, 3 g Fat, 0 g Sat Fat, 0 g Trans Fat, 43 mg Chol, 269 mg Sod, 17 g Carb, 6 g Fib, 6 g Prot, 38 mg Calc. **POINTS** value: **2.**

Hot Bean Dip with Cheddar

PREP 15 MINUTES   COOK 2 MINUTES   SERVES 4

1 (15 ½-ounce) can kidney beans, rinsed and drained
¼ cup fat-free sour cream
2 tablespoons chopped fresh cilantro
1 tablespoon lime juice
¾ teaspoon chili powder
½ teaspoon ground cumin
Pinch cayenne
¼ cup shredded fat-free cheddar cheese
4 cups assorted vegetable sticks (such as carrots, celery, and bell peppers)

1 Spray a small shallow microwavable dish with cooking spray.

2 Place the beans in a medium bowl; mash with a potato masher or a fork. Stir in the sour cream, cilantro, lime juice, chili powder, cumin, and cayenne. Spoon the dip into the prepared dish; sprinkle with the cheese. Cover loosely with waxed paper. Microwave on high until the dip is heated through and the cheese is melted, about 2 minutes. Serve at once with the vegetables.

PER SERVING (⅓ cup dip and 1 cup vegetables): 115 Cal, 1 g Fat, 0 g Sat Fat, 0 g Trans Fat, 1 mg Chol, 251 mg Sod, 21 g Carb, 7 g Fib, 8 g Prot, 144 mg Calc. **POINTS** value: **2.**

SHRIMP AND JICAMA
COCKTAIL KEBABS

Crispy Vegetable Hush Puppies

PREP 12 MINUTES   COOK 25 MINUTES   SERVES 4

2 small (4-ounce) new potatoes, peeled
2 small zucchini
2 small carrots, shredded
2 scallions, finely chopped
2 egg whites, lightly beaten
2 tablespoons all-purpose flour
1 teaspoon salt
½ teaspoon black pepper
1 tablespoon canola oil

1 Place the potatoes in a small saucepan, add water to cover, and bring to a boil. Lower the heat and simmer just until the potatoes are tender, 6–7 minutes; drain. Cover with cold water to cool.

2 Meanwhile, coarsely grate the zucchini onto a double layer of paper towels; spread out the zucchini and let stand 3 minutes to drain. Combine with the carrots, scallions, egg whites, flour, salt, and pepper in a large bowl. Drain the potatoes, pat dry, grate coarsely, and add to the zucchini mixture.

3 Heat the oil on a large nonstick griddle or in a large nonstick skillet over medium-high heat. Drop the batter onto the griddle by ¼-cup measures, making a total of 12 hush puppies in 2 batches. Cook until golden, about 3 minutes on each side.

PER SERVING (3 hush puppies): 112 Cal, 4 g Fat, 0 g Sat Fat, 0 g Trans Fat, 0 mg Chol, 622 mg Sod, 15 g Carb, 3 g Fib, 5 g Prot, 26 mg Calc. **POINTS** value: **2.**

Curried Popcorn Snack Mix

PREP 5 MINUTES   COOK 1 MINUTE   SERVES 8

1 tablespoon olive oil
½ teaspoon curry powder
½ teaspoon ground ginger
Pinch cayenne
6 cups plain air-popped popcorn
½ cup chopped mixed dried fruit
⅓ cup dry-roasted peanuts

1 Combine the oil, curry powder, ginger, and cayenne in a microwavable cup. Microwave on High until fragrant, 45–60 seconds, stopping every 15 seconds or so to stir.

2 Combine the popcorn, dried fruit, and peanuts in a large bowl. Drizzle the spice mixture over the popcorn mixture and toss gently to coat.

PER SERVING (¾ cup): 94 Cal, 5 g Fat, 1 g Sat Fat, 0 g Trans Fat, 0 mg Chol, 51 mg Sod, 11 g Carb, 2 g Fib, 2 g Prot, 10 mg Calc. **POINTS** value: **2.**

Creamy Waldorf Pasta Salad

PREP 12 MINUTES   COOK 20 MINUTES   SERVES 4

¾ cup rotini pasta
2 apples, cored and cut into ½-inch chunks
1 cup seedless grapes, halved
1 small carrot, chopped
1 celery stalk, finely chopped
2 tablespoons raisins
¼ cup fat-free mayonnaise
1½ tablespoons lemon juice
2 teaspoons honey
½ teaspoon salt
2 tablespoons toasted chopped walnuts

1 Cook the pasta according to package directions, omitting the salt if desired. Drain; rinse under cold running water and drain again. Transfer to a serving bowl. Add the apples, grapes, carrot, celery, and raisins; toss to combine.

2 Whisk the mayonnaise, lemon juice, honey, and salt in a small bowl until well blended. Add the dressing to the pasta mixture; toss gently to coat. Sprinkle with the walnuts.

PER SERVING (about ¾ cup): 194 Cal, 4 g Fat, 1 g Sat Fat, 0 g Trans Fat, 2 mg Chol, 431 mg Sod, 40 g Carb, 4 g Fib, 3 g Prot, 27 mg Calc. **POINTS** value: **3.**

Fruit and Cheese Kebabs

PREP 15 MINUTES   COOK NONE   SERVES 4

1 (6-ounce) container plain low-fat yogurt
2 tablespoons honey
½ teaspoon poppy seeds
2 medium apples, cored and cut into 12 chunks each
1 medium pear, cored and cut into 12 chunks
1 tablespoon lemon juice
1 cup seedless grapes
3 ounces fat-free mozzarella cheese, cut into 8 cubes
3 ounces fat-free sharp cheddar cheese, cut into 8 cubes

1 Combine the yogurt, honey, and poppy seeds in a small bowl and stir until blended.

2 Combine the apples and pear in a medium bowl; add the lemon juice and toss well to coat. Alternately thread the apple chunks, pear chunks, grapes, and mozzarella and cheddar cheeses on each of 8 (12-inch) wooden skewers. Serve the kebabs with the dip.

PER SERVING (2 kebabs and 3 tablespoons dip): 215 Cal, 2 g Fat, 1 g Sat Fat, 0 g Trans Fat, 7 mg Chol, 361 mg Sod, 38 g Carb, 3 g Fib, 15 g Prot, 698 mg Calc. **POINTS** value: **4.**

Phyllo Tart with Sweet Onions

PREP 10 MINUTES   COOK 40 MINUTES   SERVES 4

1   teaspoon olive oil
2   large (about ¾ pound) Vidalia or other sweet onions, thinly sliced
¼   cup water
½   teaspoon salt
8   kalamata olives, chopped
2   teaspoons chopped fresh thyme
½   teaspoon black pepper
4   (12 x 17-inch) sheets phyllo dough, thawed according to package directions
¼   cup shredded Jarlsberg cheese

1 Heat the oil in a large nonstick skillet over medium-high heat. Add the onions, water, and salt; bring to a boil. Reduce the heat and 20 minutes. Remove from the heat and stir in the olives, thyme, and pepper; cool slightly.

2 Preheat the oven to 400°F.

3 Place 1 phyllo sheet on a dry work surface (cover the remaining dough with plastic wrap to keep it moist). Spray lightly with nonstick spray. Top with a second sheet; spray lightly with nonstick spray and repeat until you have used all 4 sheets. Cut into 2 rectangles and place the rectangles on top of each other to form a stack. Roll the edges of the phyllo in to make a small rimmed edge; place on a baking sheet.

4 Spread the onion mixture evenly over the phyllo. Bake the tart until the edges are golden brown, about 20 minutes. Sprinkle with the cheese and bake until the cheese melts, about 5 minutes longer. Cut into 4 pieces.

PER SERVING (¼ tart): 182 Cal, 5 g Fat, 2 g Sat Fat, 0 g Trans Fat, 6 mg Chol, 471 mg Sod, 30 g Carb, 4 g Fib, 6 g Prot, 109 mg Calc. **POINTS** value: **3.**

Vegetable Summer Rolls

PREP 15 MINUTES   COOK NONE   SERVES 4

¼   cup reduced-sodium soy sauce
4   teaspoons seasoned rice vinegar
4   teaspoons honey
1   garlic clove, minced
2   ounces thin rice noodles
1   teaspoon Asian (dark) sesame oil
8   (6-inch) rice-paper wrappers
1   carrot, shredded
2   scallions, thinly sliced
¼   cup fresh cilantro leaves
8   basil leaves

1 Whisk together the soy sauce, vinegar, honey, and garlic in a small bowl; set aside.

2 Place the rice noodles in a large bowl and add enough boiling water to cover; let stand until the noodles soften, about 10 minutes. Drain; rinse under cold running water and drain again. Cut the noodles into 2-inch lengths and toss with the sesame oil.

3 To assemble the rolls, dip one rice-paper wrapper at a time in a bowl of warm water until softened, about 45 seconds; transfer to a clean kitchen towel. Place one eighth of the noodles, carrot, scallions, cilantro, and basil in the center of each wrapper. Fold in two opposite sides; then roll up to enclose the filling. Serve with the soy sauce mixture for dipping.

PER SERVING (2 rolls): 190 Cal, 3 g Fat, 0 g Sat Fat, 0 g Trans Fat, 0 mg Chol, 957 mg Sod, 43 g Carb, 1 g Fib, 5 g Prot, 18 mg Calc. **POINTS** value: **4.**

PHYLLO TART WITH
SWEET ONIONS

desserts

Pecan-Cappuccino Biscotti

PREP 20 MINUTES   COOK 40 MINUTES   SERVES 12

3/4 cup all-purpose flour
3 tablespoons unsweetened cocoa powder
2 teaspoons instant espresso powder
2 teaspoons cinnamon
1/2 teaspoon baking powder
1/4 teaspoon salt
1/2 cup sugar
1 large egg
1/2 teaspoon vanilla extract
1/3 cup coarsely chopped pecans

1 Preheat the oven to 350°F. Line a baking sheet with foil and spray lightly with nonstick spray.

2 Sift the flour, cocoa, espresso, cinnamon, baking powder, and salt into a bowl. Whisk together the sugar, egg, and vanilla in another bowl. Add the egg mixture to the flour mixture and stir until a dough forms. Fold in the pecans.

3 Gather the dough with lightly floured hands and transfer to a lightly floured surface. Roll into a log about 2 inches in diameter and 8 inches long. Transfer the log to the baking sheet and flatten gently until it is about 3/4 inch high. Bake until firm to the touch, 20–25 minutes.

4 Transfer the log to a cutting board and cool for about 5 minutes. With a serrated knife, cut into 12 (1/4-inch) slices. Arrange the slices on the baking sheet.

5 Reduce the oven temperature to 300°F. Bake the biscotti 10 minutes, then turn them over and bake until dried and slightly crisp, about 10 minutes longer. Transfer to a rack and cool completely. The biscotti will continue to dry out as they cool. Store in an airtight container.

PER SERVING (1 biscotti): 94 Cal, 3 g Fat, 1 g Sat Fat, 0 g Trans Fat, 18 mg Chol, 70 mg Sod, 16 g Carb, 1 g Fib, 2 g Prot, 16 mg Calc. POINTS value: 2.

Summer Melon Soup

PREP 10 MINUTES   COOK NONE   SERVES 4

1/2 medium honeydew melon, cubed (about 5 cups)
3 tablespoons sugar
1 teaspoon grated lemon zest
2 tablespoons lemon juice
2 tablespoons chopped fresh mint
1/2 cup finely chopped cantaloupe, watermelon, or honeydew

Combine the honeydew, sugar, lemon zest, lemon juice, and mint in a blender; process on high speed until pureed. Transfer to a container, cover, and refrigerate until chilled. Serve garnished with the chopped cantaloupe.

PER SERVING (1 cup): 109 Cal, 0 g Fat, 0 g Sat Fat, 0 g Trans Fat, 0 mg Chol, 47 mg Sod, 28 g Carb, 2 g Fib, 2 g Prot, 9 mg Calc. POINTS value: 2.

FROZEN YOGURT
SANDWICHES, PAGE 75

OLD-FASHIONED
CHOCOLATE MALTS, PAGE 76

PECAN-CAPPUCCINO
BISCOTTI, PAGE 72

Apricot-Almond Fool

PREP 10 MINUTES   COOK 12 MINUTES   SERVES 4

3 cups water
1 cup dried apricots
2 tablespoons sugar
1/4 teaspoon almond extract
1/4 cup light nondairy whipped topping
4 teaspoons sliced almonds

1 Bring the water, apricots, and sugar to a boil in a medium saucepan. Reduce the heat and simmer, covered, stirring occasionally, until the apricots soften, about 10 minutes. Remove from the heat and stir in the almond extract. Let cool 5 minutes.

2 Puree the apricot mixture in a food processor or blender. Transfer the puree to a medium bowl. With a rubber spatula, gently fold in the whipped topping. Cover and refrigerate at least 1 hour before serving. To serve, spoon into goblets or dessert dishes and sprinkle with the almonds.

PER SERVING (1/2 cup fool and 1 teaspoon sliced almonds): 125 Cal, 2 g Fat, 1 g Sat Fat, 0 g Trans Fat, 0 mg Chol, 9 mg Sod, 28 g Carb, 3 g Fib, 2 g Prot, 23 mg Calc. **POINTS** value: **2.**

Lemon-Mint Granita

PREP 5 MINUTES   COOK 6 MINUTES   SERVES 4

1/2 cup sugar
1/2 cup water
1 tablespoon grated lemon zest
1/2 cup lemon juice
1/4 cup chopped fresh mint

1 Bring the sugar and water to a boil in a medium saucepan; boil 5 minutes. Remove from the heat and stir in the lemon zest, lemon juice, and mint. Transfer to an 8-inch-square baking dish. Let cool 15 minutes. Cover the dish with plastic wrap and place in the freezer until the lemon mixture is partially frozen, about 2 hours.

2 Transfer the granita to a food processor or blender. Pulse 4–5 times, just until the granita is smooth (be sure not to overprocess it or it will melt). Return the granita to the baking dish. Cover and freeze until firm, 3–4 hours longer.

PER SERVING (1/2 cup): 104 Cal, 0 g Fat, 0 g Sat Fat, 0 g Trans Fat, 0 mg Chol, 8 mg Sod, 27 g Carb, 0 g Fib, 0 g Prot, 5 mg Calc. **POINTS** value: **2.**

Frozen Yogurt Sandwiches (pictured)

PREP 5 MINUTES   COOK NONE   SERVES 4

2 tablespoons sweetened flaked coconut, finely chopped
2 tablespoons pecans, finely chopped
1/2 cup vanilla fat-free frozen yogurt
8 gingersnap cookies

1 Combine the coconut and pecans on a sheet of wax paper.

2 Place a small baking sheet in the freezer. Place 2 tablespoons of the frozen yogurt on 1 cookie. Top with another cookie, gently pressing down. Working quickly, roll the cookie edges in the coconut mixture to coat, then transfer to the baking sheet. Repeat with the remaining frozen yogurt, cookies, and coconut mixture to make 4 sandwich cookies. Wrap each sandwich in plastic wrap and freeze until firm, about 1 hour.

PER SERVING (1 sandwich): 119 Cal, 4 g Fat, 1 g Sat Fat, 0 g Trans Fat, 0 mg Chol, 107 mg Sod, 17 g Carb, 1 g Fib, 2 g Prot, 52 mg Calc. **POINTS** value: **3.**

Baked White-Chocolate Soufflés

PREP 10 MINUTES   COOK 11 MINUTES   SERVES 4

4 teaspoons sugar
2 (1-ounce) squares white baking chocolate, coarsely chopped
1 tablespoon fat-free milk
1 egg yolk
1 tablespoon all-purpose flour
2 egg whites
1/4 teaspoon cream of tartar

1 Preheat the oven to 400°F. Spray 4 (4-ounce) ramekins with nonstick spray and coat the insides with 2 teaspoons of the sugar.

2 Place the chocolate and milk in a medium microwavable bowl. Microwave on High until the chocolate is melted, 30–40 seconds, stopping and stirring about every 10 seconds. Whisk in the egg yolk and flour until blended and smooth; set aside until cool.

3 With an electric mixer on medium speed, beat the egg whites and cream of tartar in a medium bowl until soft peaks form. Sprinkle with the remaining 2 teaspoons sugar and beat until glossy, about 2 minutes longer. Gently fold the beaten egg whites into the chocolate mixture.

4 Spoon the soufflé batter into the ramekins; place the cups on a small baking sheet and bake until puffed and golden, 10–15 minutes. Serve at once.

PER SERVING (1 soufflé): 125 Cal, 6 g Fat, 3 g Sat Fat, 0 g Trans Fat, 56 mg Chol, 44 mg Sod, 15 g Carb, 0 g Fib, 4 g Prot, 40 mg Calc. **POINTS** value: **3.**

Mango-Strawberry Soy Smoothies

PREP 10 MINUTES   COOK NONE   SERVES 2

1   ripe mango, peeled, seeded, and cubed
1   cup fresh strawberries, stemmed
1/2 cup vanilla reduced-fat soy milk
1/2 cup light vanilla soy yogurt
1/4 teaspoon vanilla extract
4   ice cubes

Combine the mango, strawberries, soy milk, yogurt, vanilla, and ice cubes in a blender. Process on high speed until smooth, 1–2 minutes. Divide between 2 glasses and serve at once.

PER SERVING (1 glass): 158 Cal, 2 g Fat, 0 g Sat Fat, 0 g Trans Fat, 0 mg Chol, 33 mg Sod, 35 g Carb, 4 g Fib, 3 g Prot, 207 mg Calc. **POINTS** value: **3.**

Old-Fashioned Chocolate Malts (pictured)

PREP 5 MINUTES   COOK NONE   SERVES 4

2   cups no-sugar-added chocolate fat-free ice cream
1 1/2 cups fat-free milk
2   tablespoons malt powder
2   tablespoons chocolate syrup

Combine the ice cream, milk, malt powder, and syrup in a blender. Process on high speed until smooth. Pour into 4 tall, slim glasses and serve with extra-long straws.

PER SERVING (3/4 cup): 182 Cal, 1 g Fat, 0 g Sat Fat, 0 g Trans Fat, 8 mg Chol, 181 mg Sod, 37 g Carb, 4 g Fib, 9 g Prot, 296 mg Calc. **POINTS** value: **3.**

Rice Pudding with Kiwi and Orange

PREP 10 MINUTES   COOK 18 MINUTES   SERVES 4

cups fat-free milk
cups cooked white rice
up raisins
blespoons sugar
e orange, peeled and
ed
uits, peeled and
d
easpoon vanilla extract

1 Bring the milk, rice, raisins, and sugar to a boil in a medium saucepan. Reduce the heat and simmer, uncovered, stirring often, until the pudding is thick and creamy, about 15 minutes. Meanwhile, combine the orange and kiwi fruits in a medium bowl. Set aside.

2 Remove the pudding from the heat and stir in the vanilla. Serve the pudding warm or cover and refrigerate until chilled, about 2 hours. Serve with the fruit.

PER SERVING (1/2 cup pudding and 1/2 cup fruit): 223 Cal, 1 g Fat, 0 g Sat Fat, 0 g Trans Fat, 3 mg Chol, 67 mg Sod, 49 g Carb, 3 g Fib, 7 g Prot, 195 mg Calc. **POINTS** value: **4.**

RICE PUDDING WITH
KIWI AND ORANGE

Individual Blueberry Cobbler Cups

PREP 10 MINUTES   COOK 20 MINUTES   SERVES 4

3   cups fresh blueberries
2   teaspoons minced peeled fresh ginger
2   teaspoons grated lemon zest
2   teaspoons lemon juice
1/2 teaspoon cinnamon
1/4 cup + 1 teaspoon sugar
1   cup reduced-fat baking mix
6   tablespoons fat-free milk

1 Preheat the oven to 400°F. Spray 4 (8-ounce) custard cups with nonstick spray.

2 Combine the blueberries, ginger, lemon zest, lemon juice, cinnamon, and 1/4 cup of the sugar in a medium bowl. Divide the blueberry mixture among the custard cups.

3 Combine the baking mix and milk in a medium bowl. Spoon the batter over the blueberry mixture and sprinkle with the remaining 1 teaspoon of sugar. Place the custard cups on a small baking sheet and bake until the topping is golden and the filling is bubbling, about 20 minutes. Serve warm or at room temperature.

PER SERVING (1 cobbler): 237 Cal, 3 g Fat, 1 g Sat Fat, 0 g Trans Fat, 0 mg Chol, 348 mg Sod, 51 g Carb, 4 g Fib, 4 g Prot, 65 mg Calc. **POINTS** value: **4.**

Maple-Frosted Carrot Cake

PREP 20 MINUTES   COOK 25 MINUTES   SERVES 12

1 1/2 cups cake flour
1 1/2 teaspoons baking powder
1   teaspoon cinnamon
1/2 teaspoon baking soda
1/2 teaspoon salt
3/4 cup granulated sugar
1   large egg
1   egg white
2   tablespoons canola oil
1   (8-ounce) can crushed pineapple, drained, 1/4 cup of the liquid reserved
2   carrots, shredded
1/4 cup raisins
4   ounces light cream cheese
1/4 cup confectioners' sugar
1   tablespoon maple syrup

1 Preheat the oven to 350°F. Spray an 8-inch-square baking pan with nonstick spray.

2 Sift the flour, baking powder, cinnamon, baking soda, and salt into a medium bowl.

3 Combine the granulated sugar, egg, egg white, and oil in a large bowl and stir until blended. Add the flour mixture and stir just until combined. Stir in the pineapple and reserved liquid, carrots, and raisins. Scrape the batter into the pan. Bake until a toothpick inserted into the center comes out clean, 25–30 minutes. Cool the cake in the pan on a rack for 10 minutes. Remove the cake from the pan and cool completely on the rack.

4 Beat the cream cheese, confectioners' sugar, and maple syrup in a medium bowl just until blended and smooth. Spread on top of the cooled cake. Cut into 12 squares.

PER SERVING (1/12 cake): 202 Cal, 5 g Fat, 2 g Sat Fat, 0 g Trans Fat, 25 mg Chol, 264 mg Sod, 27 g Carb, 1 g Fib, 3 g Prot, 56 mg Calc. **POINTS** value: **4.**

MAPLE-FROSTED
CARROT CAKE

MEXICAN SEVEN-LAYER SALAD
(LUNCH, *5 POINTS* value)

Dry and Liquid Measurement Equivalents

If you are converting the recipes in this book to metric measurements, use the following chart as a guide.

TEASPOONS	TABLESPOONS	CUPS	FLUID OUNCES
3 teaspoons	1 tablespoon		½ fluid ounce
6 teaspoons	2 tablespoons	⅛ cup	1 fluid ounce
8 teaspoons	2 tablespoons plus 2 teaspoons	⅙ cup	
12 teaspoons	4 tablespoons	¼ cup	2 fluid ounces
15 teaspoons	5 tablespoons	⅓ cup minus 1 teaspoon	
16 teaspoons	5 tablespoons plus 1 teaspoon	⅓ cup	
18 teaspoons	6 tablespoons	¼ cup plus 2 tablespoons	3 fluid ounces
24 teaspoons	8 tablespoons	½ cup	4 fluid ounces
30 teaspoons	10 tablespoons	½ cup plus 2 tablespoons	5 fluid ounces
32 teaspoons	10 tablespoons plus 2 teaspoons	⅔ cup	
36 teaspoons	12 tablespoons	¾ cup	6 fluid ounces
42 teaspoons	14 tablespoons	1 cup minus 2 tablespoons	7 fluid ounces
45 teaspoons	15 tablespoons	1 cup minus 1 tablespoon	
48 teaspoons	16 tablespoons	1 cup	8 fluid ounces

VOLUME	
¼ teaspoon	1 milliliter
½ teaspoon	2 milliliters
1 teaspoon	5 milliliters
1 tablespoon	15 milliliters
2 tablespoons	30 milliliters
3 tablespoons	45 milliliters
¼ cup	60 milliliters
⅓ cup	80 milliliters
½ cup	120 milliliters
⅔ cup	160 milliliters
¾ cup	175 milliliters
1 cup	240 milliliters
1 quart	950 milliliters

LENGTH	
1 inch	25 millimeters
1 inch	2.5 centimeters

OVEN TEMPERATURE			
250°F	120°C	400°F	200°C
275°F	140°C	425°F	220°C
300°F	150°C	450°F	230°C
325°F	160°C	475°F	250°C
350°F	180°C	500°F	260°C
375°F	190°C	525°F	270°C

WEIGHT	
1 ounce	30 grams
¼ pound	120 grams
½ pound	240 grams
1 pound	480 grams

NOTE: Measurement of less than ⅛ teaspoon is considered a dash or a pinch. Metric volume measurements are approximate.

POINTS value Recipe Index

BREAKFAST

2 POINTS value

New York–Style Eggs and Lox

3 POINTS value

Greek Isle Breakfast Skillet

Peach and Ginger Crêpes

Bran Muffins with Apple and Walnuts

Cherry-Orange Scones

4 POINTS value

Denver-Style Shirred Eggs

Shrimp and Vegetable Frittata

Mozzarella and Tomato Strata

Vegetable Hash with Eggs

Fresh Berry Blintzes

Honey Granola

Sausage-Buttermilk Corn Bread

Spiced Pumpkin Breakfast Bread

5 POINTS value

Peach Breakfast Smoothie

Caramelized Oatmeal with Yogurt

Citrus-Cinnamon Breakfast Apples

Creamy Barley with Fresh Fruit Salsa

Risotto-Style Rice Porridge

6 POINTS value

Huevos Rancheros with Avocado

Banana-Buttermilk Pancakes

Waffles with Caramelized Apples

Spicy Black Bean and Spinach Omelette

Stuffed French Toast

Irish Oatmeal with Dried Fruit

7 POINTS value

Oat Pancakes with Blueberry Sauce

LUNCH

3 POINTS value

Turkey, Orange, and Fennel Salad

Sausage and Spinach Roll-ups

Salmon Salad Wraps

4 POINTS value

Updated Bistro Salad

Spicy Thai-Style Turkey Wraps

Chunky Clam Chowder

Mexican Bean Soup with Tortilla Chips

Chickpea and Barley Salad

Potato and Bacon Soup

Summer-Style Stuffed Tomatoes

Hummus and Salad Pitas

5 POINTS value

Caribbean Beef Rolls with Papaya Salsa

Mexican Seven-Layer Salad

Asian Cabbage Slaw with Pork

Chicken and Edamame Salad

Salmon Cakes with Herb Sauce

South-of-the-Border Tuna Burrito Rolls

Dilled Tuna Sandwiches

Italian Tortellini Salad

Mesclun Pizza with Pears

6 POINTS value

Hearty Avgolemono Soup

Curried Couscous Salad with Chicken

Quesadillas with Spinach and Crab

Crunchy Peanut Noodles with Tofu

7 POINTS value

Chicken and Prosciutto Heroes

DINNER

4 POINTS value

Pomegranate-Glazed Shish Kebabs

Scaloppine with Asparagus

Barbecued Drumsticks

Chicken Sausage Ragu over Polenta

Grilled Snapper with Chili-Lime Butter

Tex-Mex Shrimp Stew

Tofu and Asparagus in Coconut Sauce

5 POINTS value

Garlicky Lamb Chops with Snap Peas

Thai Curry with Chicken and Cauliflower

Maple-Glazed Cornish Hens with Carrots

Peking-Style Duck Wraps

Spicy Bean Patties with Cilantro Cream

Indian-Spiced Red Lentil Stew

6 POINTS value

Steak with Onion and Potato Cakes

Pork with Mushroom-Roquefort Sauce

Lamb Tagine with Apricots

Baked Potatoes with Chili

Turkey Cutlets with Pecan Topping

Soy-Marinated Tuna over Ginger Slaw

Mussels in Garlicky Sauce with Linguine

Orzo with Broccoli and Pine Nuts

7 POINTS value

Pork Chops with Spiced Squash Puree

Lemon-Thyme Chicken with Potatoes

Spaghetti with Shrimp and White Beans

Miso Soup with Scallops and Noodles

SNACKS

1 POINTS value

Salmon Dip with Cucumbers

Stuffed Plum Tomatoes

Quick Avocado Salsa

Spiced Edamame

2 POINTS value

Stuffed Portobello Mushroom Caps

Citrus-Snapper Seviche

Shrimp and Jicama Cocktail Kebabs

Hot Bean Dip with Cheddar

Crispy Vegetable Hush Puppies

Curried Popcorn Snack Mix

3 POINTS value

Creamy Waldorf Pasta Salad

Phyllo Tart with Sweet Onion

4 POINTS value

Fruit and Cheese Kebabs

Vegetable Summer Rolls

DESSERTS

2 POINTS value

Pecan-Cappuccino Biscotti

Summer Melon Soup

Apricot-Almond Fool

Lemon-Mint Granita

3 POINTS value

Frozen Yogurt Sandwiches

Baked White-Chocolate Soufflés

Mango-Strawberry Soy Smoothies

Old-Fashioned Chocolate Malt

4 POINTS value

Rice Pudding with Kiwi and Orange

Individual Blueberry Cobbler Cups

Maple-Frosted Carrot Cake

Core Plan Recipe Index

BREAKFAST

New York–Style Eggs and Lox ✓

Denver-Style Shirred Eggs ✓

Shrimp and Vegetable Frittata ✓

Vegetable Hash with Eggs ✓

Citrus-Cinnamon Breakfast Apples ✓

Creamy Barley with Fresh Fruit Salsa ✓

LUNCH

Turkey, Orange, and Fennel Salad ✓

Updated Bistro Salad ✓

Chunky Clam Chowder ✓

Chickpea and Barley Salad ✓

Summer-Style Stuffed Tomatoes ✓

Mexican Seven-Layer Salad ✓

Curried Couscous Salad with Chicken ✓

DINNER

Tex-Mex Shrimp Stew ✓

Garlicky Lamb Chops with Snap Peas ✓

Spicy Bean Patties with Cilantro Cream ✓

Indian-Spiced Red Lentil Stew ✓

Steak with Onion and Potato Cakes ✓

Baked Potatoes with Chili ✓

Lemon-Thyme Chicken with Potatoes ✓

Spaghetti with Shrimp and White Beans ✓

SNACKS

Salmon Dip with Cucumbers ✓

Stuffed Plum Tomatoes ✓

Quick Avocado Salsa ✓

Spiced Edamame ✓

Citrus-Snapper Seviche ✓

Hot Bean Dip with Cheddar ✓

SUMMER-STYLE STUFFED TOMATOES

(LUNCH, *4 POINTS* value)

Notes

Notes